ISBN 978-1-7336637-0-0

9 781733 663700 >

MILO'S MISSION TO THE MOON

BY

C. L. MONTGOMERY

ISBN: 978-1-7336637-0-0 (Paperback)
Library of Congress Control Number: 2019903212

Any references to historical events, real people, or real places are used fictitiously. Names, characters, and places are products of the author's imagination.

Author: Cassandra L. Montgomery. Also known as: C.L. Montgomery
Illustrated By: Scot Mmobuosi
Editor: A. Ashiru

Ordering Information:
Quantity sales. Special discounts are available on quantity purchases by corporations, associations, and others. For details, contact the publisher at the address above. Orders by U.S. trade bookstores and wholesalers. Please contact BDKZ Distribution: Tel: (770)-572-2755; Fax: (770) 572-2755. Email:info@clmontgomery.com.

Published by BDKZ Publishing, LLC
P.O.Box 311530
Atlanta GA 31131

Printed in the United States of America

First Edition

Inspiration

This book is dedicated to Maurice Lincoln Overby II, my son, and every other kid in the universe who loves everything science and LEGO. The fundamentals of learning for children became very important to me once I became a mother, especially to such an inquisitive kid who asked a ton of questions such as: "Mommy, is the sun following us?" or "Where is the moon tonight?"

Who could have known that a new mom would have to tackle such sweeping questions from a very adamant and demanding 4-year-old? Well, trust me, the stories and "theories" we both came up with to expand his imagination were creative, exciting, and fun. And that is how learning should be!

We want to share these experiences with the world with hopes that children all over the world can have fun and get lost in their own imagination while learning about the Moon, the Stars, the Sun, the Solar System, and everything in our Universe!

Thank you for purchasing a copy of our book. We truly appreciate each and every one of you! I hope you enjoy it as much as Milo and I enjoy sharing our stories.

Love,
MILO, and Mommy!

I found a broom;
I'm going to Zoom Zoom Zoom,
All the way to the moon!

Up, up and Away,
I will touch the moon's face,
Take a piece of it,
And bring it home to play.

New Moon   Waxing Crescent   First Quarter   Waxing Gibbous   Full Moon   waning Gibbous   Last Quarter   Waning Crescent

Geesh! My mom said the moon is far far far away,

238,835 miles from the Planet Earth today.

Hmm, who cares? I'm going anyway,

Let me plan my journey, I'm going to go all the way!

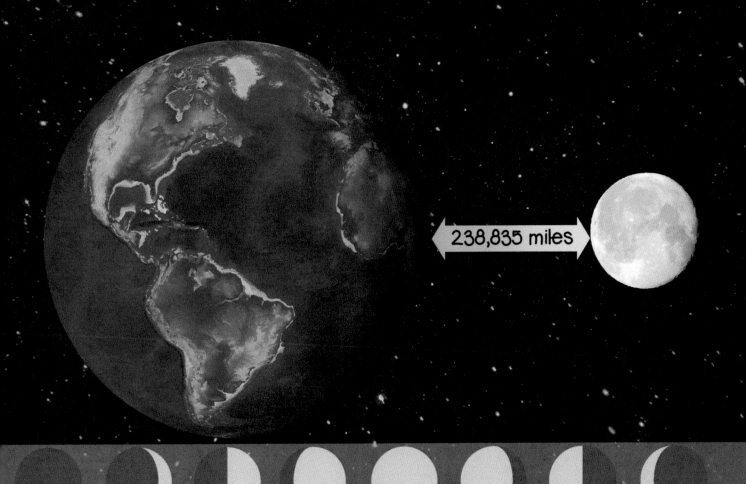

I'll put on my shoes and wear my coat,
This mission is not a joke,
What should I take? A car, plane, jet, or a boat?

New Moon Waxing Crescent First Quarter Waxing Gibbous Full Moon waning Gibbous Last Quarter Waning Crescent

But wait! To get through space,
I'll need another way.
Maybe I should make a rocket ship out of clay,
Or a magic rug like a genie and float through space,
I can jump on a trampoline and go up, up, and away!

New Moon   Waxing Crescent   First Quarter   Waxing Gibbous   Full Moon   waning Gibbous   Last Quarter   Waning Crescent

I'm all set. Time for take off!

I looked up, but the moon was lost,

It was GONE and the midnight sky wasn't bright.

Oh NO! I'm freaking out, the moon was out of sight;

My mission is ruined! My plan was to leave tonight.

New Moon   Waxing Crescent   First Quarter   Waxing Gibbous   Full Moon   waning Gibbous   Last Quarter   Waning Crescent

What happened? This moon I have to find!
I have to get my mom; I'm running out of time!

"Mom, Mom, get up! Get up!
Please help! I'm out of luck,
The moon has disappeared,
The sky is dark; I'm really scared!"

New Moon   Waxing Crescent   First Quarter   Waxing Gibbous   Full Moon   waning Gibbous   Last Quarter   Waning Crescent

"Honey, Honey, calm down, don't frown,
The moon is in one of its mysterious magical phases.
It moves and trades places.
It orbits the Earth which takes almost 30 days.
No need to worry or be in a hurry!"

"So it's magical, like a Jack in the Hat that won't come back?
Like a rabbit in a hat that's lost in a sac?
Or a duck you can't see, but you can hear it quack?"

First Quarter

Waxing Gibbous

Waxing Crescent

Full

New

Waning Gibbous

Waning Crescent

Third Quarter

| New Moon | Waxing Crescent | First Quarter | Waxing Gibbous | Full Moon | waning Gibbous | Last Quarter | Waning Crescent |

"Milo, you're so funny, sit down, Honey.

Let me explain, using our tummies!

Let's say the moon is a pizza pie."

"Ummm, Mommy, it sounds so yummy!

Yum! Yum! Yum, now I'm hungry!

Pizza, Pizza, GET IN MY TUMMY!"

 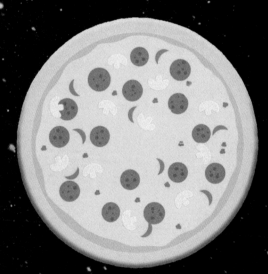

New Moon   Waxing Crescent   First Quarter   Waxing Gibbous   Full Moon   waning Gibbous   Last Quarter   Waning Crescent

"The 1st phase of the moon is the New Moon.

It looks like a cheese pizza, eaten till it's gone."

"Mommy, did Dad and I eat it up from you?"

"Ha-ha! Oh, Milo, how wrong are you!"

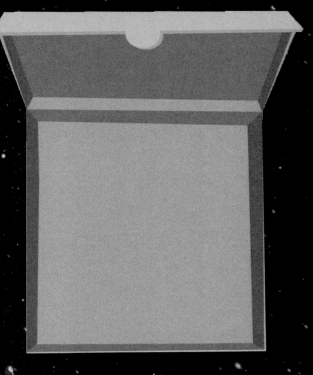

New Moon Waxing Crescent First Quarter Waxing Gibbous Full Moon waning Gibbous Last Quarter Waning Crescent

"The 2nd phase is called the Waxing Crescent.

Well, we gobbled up some cheesy slices, but the crust on the right didn't make it!"

"Make it where, Mommy? In my yummy, yummy tummy?

Ha ha ha ha!!! Mommy, you're so funny!"

| New Moon | Waxing Crescent | First Quarter | Waxing Gibbous | Full Moon | waning Gibbous | Last Quarter | Waning Crescent |

"The 3rd phase is called the First Quarter Moon.

Our tummies have lots of room,

We ate one half of our pizza pie,

Precisely, the entire LEFT side. Oh my, my, my!!

Someone has a bigger tummy.

Hmmm, I wonder who!"

New Moon   Waxing Crescent   First Quarter   Waxing Gibbous   Full Moon   waning Gibbous   Last Quarter   Waning Crescent

"Guess what phase is next?
It's what you like best;
Waxing Gibbous Moon.
Who ate the left side of the pizza crust,
And went to their room?"

"Never to be found and never to return! BWAHAHA!!"

"Wait! Wait! You said what, Mommy? Waxing Gibbous?
That sounds like a spooky Halloween night of horrors!
Full of fright, ghosts, and goblins which I don't like,
Or ghost and gloom! Now that will make me take a hike!"

"What's next, please? Go fast... Hurry! Hurry! Let's MOVE ON!"

New Moon   Waxing Crescent   First Quarter   Waxing Gibbous   Full Moon   waning Gibbous   Last Quarter   Waning Crescent

"My favorite is next! A Full Moon! It shines so bright; it lights up the sky.

It's a whole sweet, delicious cheesy, peezy, weezy pizza pie!

That's until you or your dad tries to take a slice."

"And find a place to hide? Hahaha!"

New Moon   Waxing Crescent   First Quarter   Waxing Gibbous   Full Moon   waning Gibbous   Last Quarter   Waning Crescent

"The next adventure is our Waning Gibbous Moon,"

"Wait, Mom! Isn't that the spooky moon, are you sure it's moved on?"

"Look closely, a little closer, look at the crust!
See the right side is gone; let's just say you couldn't hold on,
Thus, a bite is a must!"

"Oh no, Mom, I need the entire slice, or I will fuss.
Remember, my tummy has lots of room,
Though I know I can eat an entire Waning Gibbous Moon!"

| New Moon | Waxing Crescent | First Quarter | Waxing Gibbous | Full Moon | waning Gibbous | Last Quarter | Waning Crescent |

"In our 7th phase as the moon orbits the Earth; we have reached the Last Quarter Moon. Now, you little pizza eater, you've eaten half of the pizza pie;
The entire right side! You crept into the kitchen in the middle of the night."

"And guess what, you weren't even afraid because you had a flashlight!"

"Bwahahahaha! Milo, that was funny, right?"

New Moon   Waxing Crescent   First Quarter   Waxing Gibbous   Full Moon   waning Gibbous   Last Quarter   Waning Crescent

"Well, I'll get you back, Mommy. It's revenge time,
And our next phase will give me mine!
The Waning Crescent proves that I ate so fast and left you in the dust,
And that I only saved you the stuffed left side of the pizza crust!!!
Haha! I'm stuffed!"

"Oh no, Milo, Mommy wins again and again.
I'm the one who pays the pizza man! HA HA!
Well, that's all for now until the phases start all over again!"

New Moon   Waxing Crescent   First Quarter   Waxing Gibbous   Full Moon   waning Gibbous   Last Quarter   Waning Crescent

"Well then off to the moon I go, and when I land,
It's going to be grand,
CAUSE I'M THE MAN! And very tall, I'll stand.
I'm going to wheel up the Waxing Crescent Moon on a dirt bike,
Flip around like it's a ramp with bright lights,
Take a piece of it, and travel back in a couple of nights!"

"Oh, Milo, that sounds quite like the adventure.
You make sure you hold on tight!
Have fun, my son, I will see you upon your return.
Now, please get some rest,
I hope you enjoyed learning about the moon's magical quest!"

New Moon   Waxing Crescent   First Quarter   Waxing Gibbous   Full Moon   waning Gibbous   Last Quarter   Waning Crescent

"Ok, Mommy, but I really love the moon; it's so exciting! Look, I got it!

The Waxing Gibbous is the opposite of the Waning Gibbous.

The Waxing Crescent is the opposite of the Waning Crescent.

The First Quarter is the opposite of the Last Quarter Moon,

And the New Moon is the opposite of the Full Moon - this one is like Night and Day!"

Hey, the moon is not a mystery, I want to chase it day by day.

Phase after phase I'll chase, as it orbits through space.

This will take around a month, or maybe 29 days!

That's more time to play!!!

WAXING CRESCENT

NEW MOON

WANING CRESCENT

FIRST QUARTER

LAST QUARTER

WAXING GIBBOUS

FULL MOON

WANING GIBBOUS

New Moon   Waxing Crescent   First Quarter   Waxing Gibbous   Full Moon   waning Gibbous   Last Quarter   Waning Crescent

I can stop it... I can rock it; I can poke it, I can pop it.

I can bite it; I can chop it, I can ride it, like a rocket!

"I wonder how far I will be from the sun. THE SUN MOMMY, THE SUN!"

"Yes, Honey."

Will the sun burn? Hmmmmm, my next journey has just begun!

New Moon   Waxing Crescent   First Quarter   Waxing Gibbous   Full Moon   waning Gibbous   Last Quarter   Waning Crescent

Meet Milo!

This is one inquisitive kiddo! He's a determined kid with a big, imaginative mind! Everyone calls him nicknames like, the Scientist, the Professor, the Astronaut, and the Inventor! He is always willing to help his peers!

This kiddo researches everything from the moon to the Egyptian Pyramids. Milo is an honor student, and he is destined to become someone who will impact this world! In his spare time, he loves reading, experimenting, and everything LEGO!!! This kid is Scientifically B.A.D.D. *(Brilliant.Ambitious.Dynamic.Driven)*!

Do you think Milo is Super Cool? Order Milo's T-shirt to represent your coolness, too! **www.SchoolOfBadd.com!**

THANK YOU FOR SUPPORTING MILO'S MISSIONS!

PLEASE BE ON THE LOOK OUT FOR ADVENTURES TO COME!

C.L. MONTGOMERY

Made in the USA
Middletown, DE
22 December 2019